CW00840634

The Birds Down the Lane

words and pictures by
Carl A Mynott

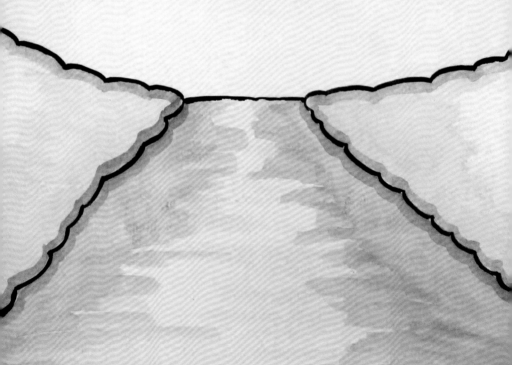

The Birds Down the Lane

Copyright © 2014 by Carl A Mynott

The rights of Carl A Mynott to be identified as author, illustrator and publisher of this work have been asserted by him in accordance with the Copyright, Designs and Patents Act, 1988.

First edition published by the author in November 2014.

All rights reserved.

ISBN 978-0-9929398-1-6

Carl A Mynott
www.britishwildlifetales.co.uk
info@britishwildlifetales.co.uk

for Linda

The little one smiles and
wipes their mouth on a sleeve

"Thanks for the lunch Daddy
now can we leave?"

the washing up's done
the plates put away

they head out the back gate
it's such a bright day

no need for a coat
there's no sign of rain

it's time for a walk with the
birds down the lane

The hedge is alive
it's a bush full of tweets

there's a roost of House Sparrows
down the lane where they meet

one bird flies out
and over the top

back into the garden
to eat till he pops

a brown and grey bird
with a beard of black fluff

you'll see him and his friends
roll around in the dust

As the family walks
something darts from the tree

then one more shoots out
and another makes three

they jump between bushes
they're called Long-tailed Tits

a train of sweet birds
just like lollipop sticks

they have black and brown backs
with pinkish-white chests

teeny tiny small things
their long tail is the best

Daddy says "Wait!
Can you hear? What's that sound?"

"pink pink!" chirps a bird
and they all look around

Chaffinch appears
with his steely grey hat

his chest is all pink
and his wife will be sat

nearby in the trees
with her feathers all brown

so he sings to her there
then pecks food from the ground

Around the next bend
in the lane there's a tree

all covered in ivy
with shiny green leaves

nesting inside
is a tiny brown bird

whose powerful voice
you will no doubt have heard

right then Wren appears
but she zips through the air

and then disappears quickly
like she never was there

There's a big old pine tree
down the lane near the church

a Greenfinch lives there
and this tree is his perch

when his lady appears
on a branch of the tree

he sings his best song
with some chirps then a "wheeeeeee"

his feathers are green
from his beak to his toes

he flies up to the treetop
to complete his grand show

Mummy shouts out
"two for joy" when she sees

a pair of Magpies
flying down from the trees

black and white from afar
then when one comes near

the sun shines on her back
and the colours appear

blue and green on her tail
and purple on her back

white on both sides
and her head is jet black

Something pointy emerges
from the chimney pot top

a Jackdaw jumps out
along the roof in three hops

with shiny black feathers
and a silver-grey neck

her beady steel eyes
search for something to peck

she heads down the tiles
and jabs at the moss

she struts when she walks
just like she's the boss

Around the next bend
a loud noise drums the air

in the huge tall birch tree
is a bird pecking there

with a black and white coat
and a splash of bright red

a Great Spotted Woodpecker
bangs the tree with his head

the little one draws closer
but the bird climbs around

to the back of the tree
where he'll never be found

Ahead there's a verge
wide grassy and green

where field voles and mice
and weasels are seen

by a Kestrel up high
above where she hovers

if she catches them here
they're in all sorts of bother

she'll eat them for dinner
or maybe for lunch

and then take what's left
for her babies to munch

Back at the house
there's a bird smashing shells

on the wall by the shed
to the sound of church bells

the Song Thrush sings out
the same song a few times

then he changes his song
and repeats his new lines

brown on his back
and spots on his tummy

he gulps down some snails
they're ever so yummy

The little one walks in
Mummy closes the gate

they head through the kitchen
they're a tiny bit late

"what's that you're doing?"
Daddy says as he looks

Little one replies
"I'm just checking my books..."

"...to see if the colours
of the birds are the same..."

"...as the ones I have seen
on the birds down the lane".

Help your Mummies and Daddies

How to get your parents to take you outdoors...

It's sometimes quite hard
to get parents outside

they're so busy doing stuff
that keeps them inside

so pick up your toys
and tidy your room

and then they will find
there is much less to do

no more packing away
no more clearing the floors

and more time to go out
in the great wild outdoors.

How to watch for
The Birds Down the Lane...

The first things you need
are two beady eyes

you will use them to search
through the trees and the skies

the next thing you will need
are your left and right ear

when the birds start to sing
these will help you to hear

then a pen and a pad
will help you take notes

and the last thing you will need
is a hat, and a coat

Which of the Birds Down the Lane have you seen?

Have you seen a House Sparrow? ○

Have you seen a Long-tailed Tit? ○

Have you seen a Chaffinch? ○

Have you seen a Wren? ○

Have you seen Greenfinch? ○

Have you seen a Magpie? ○

Have you seen a Jackdaw? ○

Have you seen a Great Spotted Woodpecker? ○

Have you seen a Kestrel? ○

Have you seen a Song Thrush? ○

There are many things in life that are important.

Two of them inspired me to begin creating these books.

They are:

My family.

The natural world.

___

If you do just two things in life, do these:

Love your family

and

Teach them about the natural world.

You're already doing one of them, Thank you for buying my book.

Carl.

BOOKS IN THE BRITISH WILDLIFE TALES SERIES

AVAILABLE NOW

'The Birds at the Bottom of the Garden'
ISBN: 978-0 9929398-0-9

'The Birds Down the Lane'
ISBN: 978-0-9929398-1-6

COMING SOON

'What's in the Wood pile?'
featuring 10 fantastic creatures
from mini-beasts and mammals
to molluscs and reptiles!

FUTURE TITLES

For more information, and for details about future titles
please visit the British Wildlife Tales website at:

www.britishwildlifetales.co.uk